Contents

Dee Reid

Story illustrated by
Marcelo Baez

Before Reading

Find out about

- How a pharaoh of ancient Egypt was buried in a pyramid

Tricky words

- Egypt
- pyramid
- Pharaoh Cheops (*say Kee-ops*)
- buried
- kohl
- sarcophagus
- mummified
- funeral

Text starter

Read about Amon, who lived in Egypt in 2566 BC. He is going with his father to see old Pharaoh Cheops buried in a sarcophagus in a tomb in the pyramid at Giza. Amon knows that the Pharaoh's body has been mummified so that he can keep it in the afterlife.

My name is Amon. I live in Egypt. Today is a very big day for me because my father is taking me to the pyramid at Giza. The Pharaoh Cheops will be buried in it.

I had a bath to get ready for our big day out. My slave poured jugs of water over me until I was clean. When I was dry I rubbed special oil into my skin.

Next I had to put on my make-up. I wear eye paint called kohl to make my eyes look special.

Then I had breakfast with my father.
We ate bread and honey. The slave
brought us wine to drink.
After breakfast we set off for Giza.

The streets are very crowded. Lots of people are going to the pyramid. We will see the sarcophagus of the Pharaoh being taken into the pyramid.

The white stones gleam in the sunlight. I have seen the pyramid many times but today is special because the Pharaoh is to be buried.

Pharaoh Cheops died eight weeks ago. His body has been mummified. That means it will not decay, so he can keep his body in the afterlife.

Father says they use a hook to pull out the brain through the nose! Yuk!

Father and I stand by the ramp.
Now we hear the sound of horns.
The funeral is beginning. We watch the sarcophagus being carried into the pyramid.

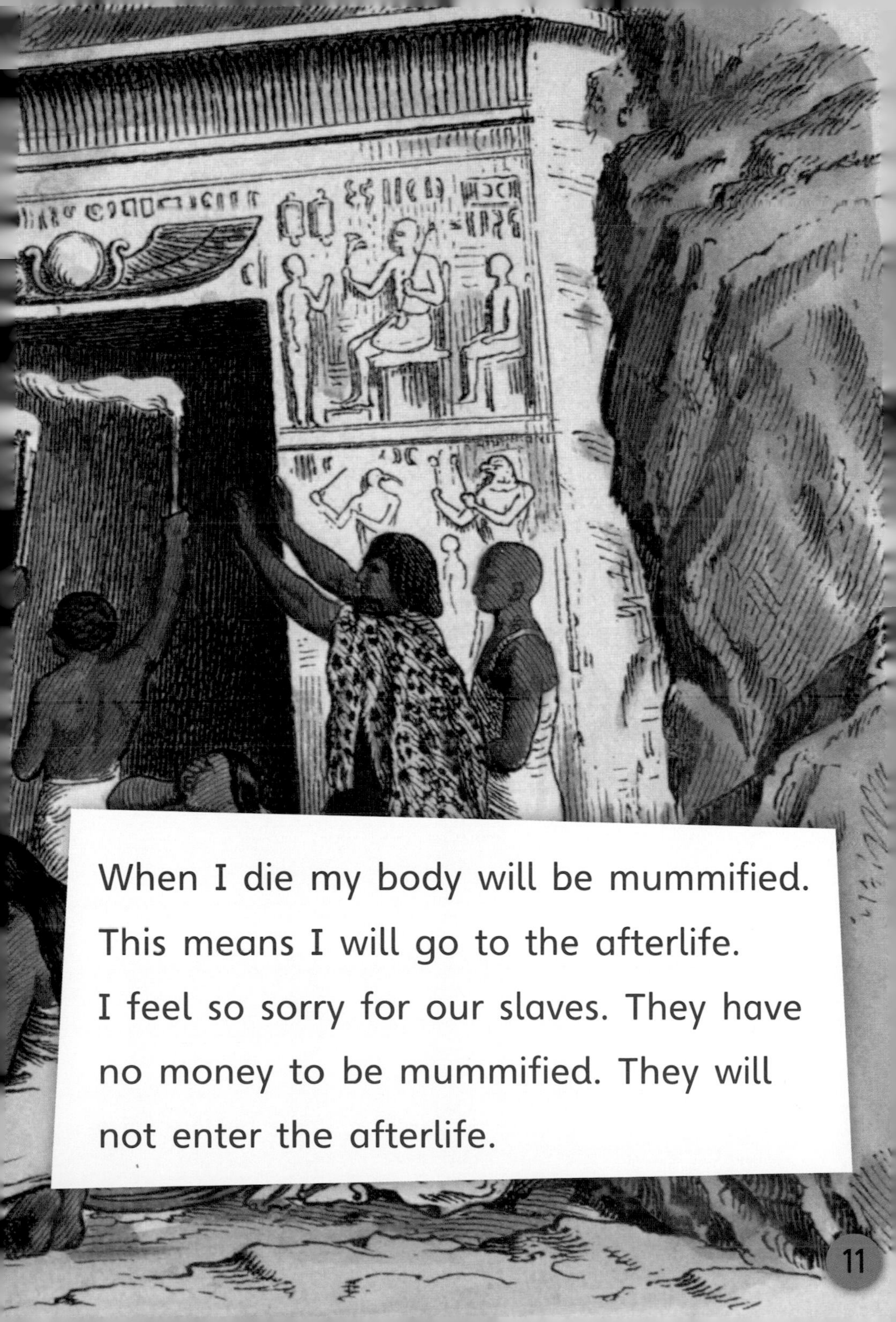

When I die my body will be mummified. This means I will go to the afterlife. I feel so sorry for our slaves. They have no money to be mummified. They will not enter the afterlife.

We are not allowed to go up into the tomb. It is a secret where the tomb is. All maps have been torn up. So no one will ever find the tomb.

I ask Father about the slaves who took the treasure into the tomb. They must know where the tomb is. Father tells me that the slaves are shut up in the tomb so that they cannot give away the secret.

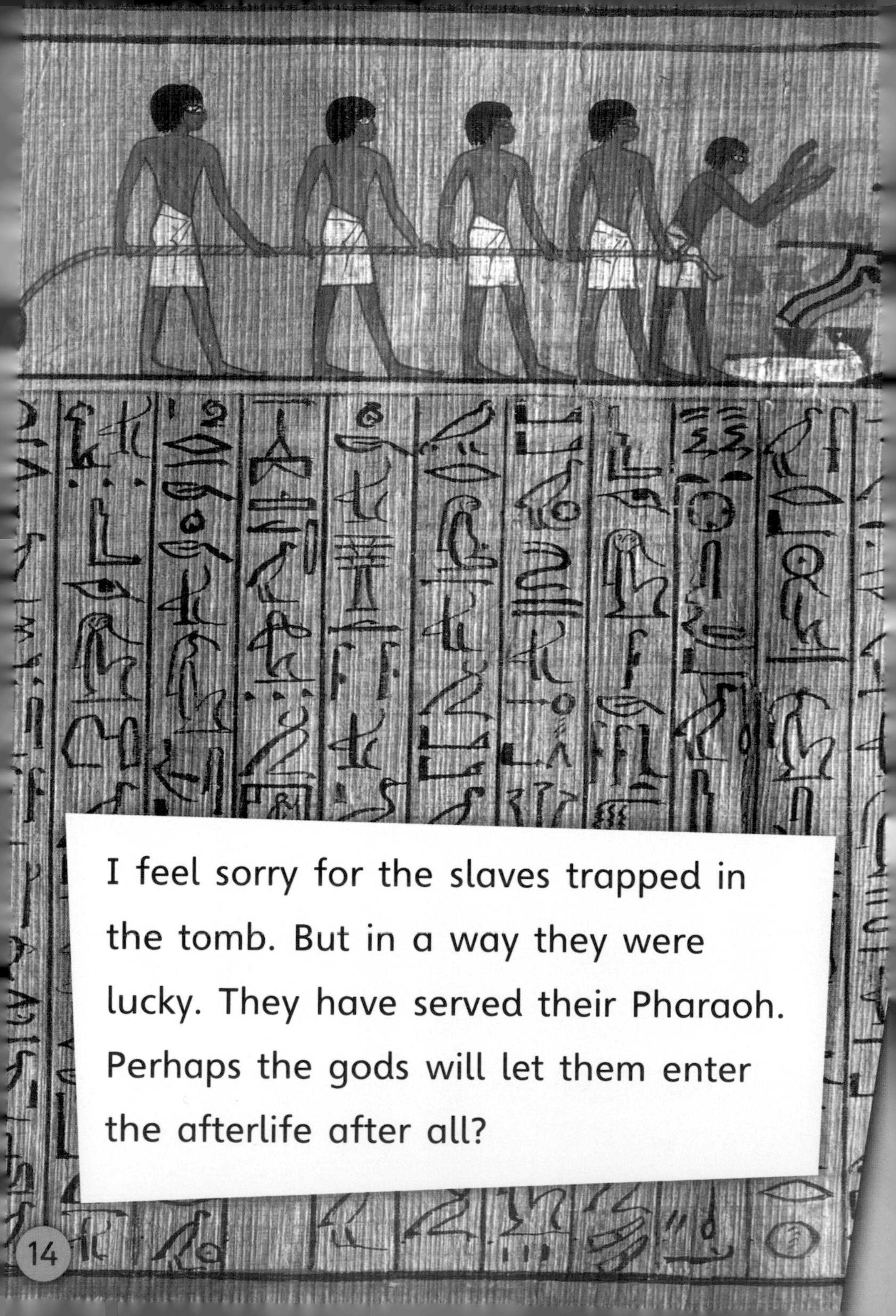

I feel sorry for the slaves trapped in the tomb. But in a way they were lucky. They have served their Pharaoh. Perhaps the gods will let them enter the afterlife after all?

Quiz

Text Detective

- What happened to the slaves who helped to bury the Pharaoh?
- Would you like to have lived in ancient Egypt?

Word Detective

- **Phonic Focus:** Identifying long- and short-vowel phonemes
  Page 3: How many syllables are there in the word 'taking'? Is the vowel phoneme in each syllable long or short?
- Page 7: Find a word that means 'busy'.
- Page 11: Find a compound word.

Super Speller

Read these words:

being carried cannot

Now try to spell them!

HA! HA! HA!

Q Which ancient Egyptian king was good at washing up?

Pharaoh Liquid!

Before Reading

In this story

Scott

Omar

The Master

Tricky words

- mirror
- wearing
- clothes
- pyramid
- treasure
- tomb
- pieces
- gleam

Story starter

Scott's gran had found an old mirror in her attic. She gave it to Scott and he hung it up on his bedroom wall. But when Scott looked in the old mirror, something very strange happened – the boy in the mirror wasn't Scott!

Scott and the Tomb

Scott looked in the old mirror.
Someone looked back at him.
The boy in the mirror looked a bit like Scott but he wasn't Scott and he was wearing very strange clothes.

"Come on," said the boy in the mirror, "or we'll be late."
Scott stepped forward and felt himself falling into the mirror!

Scott looked around. Lots of people were pulling heavy stones up a long slope on a pyramid!

Then a man came up to them.

"Omar," he said, "you are late! Is this the new slave?"

"Yes, Master," said Omar.

"Can he keep a secret?" said the man.

"Yes, he can keep a secret," said Omar.

“Why is he wearing such strange clothes?” asked the man.

“I don’t know,” said Omar.

“Well, pick up this box,” said the man.

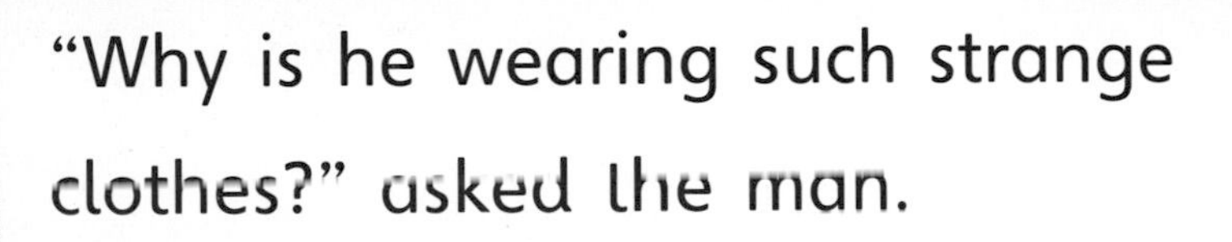

Scott and Omar followed the man up the slope.

"This box is full of treasure. It will be hidden in the tomb," whispered Omar, "and we must keep the tomb secret."

"I've got a bad feeling about this," thought Scott.

Then Scott remembered reading that the slaves who carried the treasure were trapped inside the tomb so the secret could be kept.

"I've got a ***very*** bad feeling about this," thought Scott.

They went into the pyramid. Then they passed some old men who were looking at some pieces of paper. Scott picked up a piece of paper from the floor.

They came to a hole in the wall.
"Take the treasure up into the tomb," said the man, "and here is a gold coin for each of you."
"Now my family will be rich," said Omar.

But when they got to the tomb, the man shouted to them. "You will keep the secret because you will never get out!"

Then the man pushed a heavy stone across the hole in the wall.

"Now I will die here," said Omar, "and my family will never be rich!"

"Look at this," said Scott and he gave Omar the piece of paper he had picked up. It was a map of the tunnels and it showed a way out.

Scott and Omar pulled out a loose stone in the wall and found a tunnel. It led them out of the pyramid.

"I was right," said Omar. "You can keep a secret! You have saved my life!" Scott gave Omar his gold coin, but then something very strange happened. The sun shone on the coin and made it gleam like a mirror. Scott looked at the coin and felt himself falling forwards.

Scott was back in his bedroom, looking at his old mirror. The person looking back at Scott was Scott.

"Strange," thought Scott, as he felt the map in his pocket.

Quiz

Text Detective

- How did Scott find a way out of the pyramid?
- What do you think Omar did after he escaped?

Word Detective

- **Phonic Focus:** Identifying long- and short-vowel phonemes
  Page 20: How many syllables are there in the word 'secret'? Is the vowel phoneme in each syllable long or short?
- Page 23: Find a word that means the opposite of 'forgot'.
- Page 23: Why is the word 'very' in bold print?

Super Speller

Read these words:

hidden rich loose

Now try to spell them!

HA! HA! HA!

Q Why was the Egyptian boy confused?

Because he thought his daddy was a mummy!